4

BAM
SPLAT,
AND
BLOOIE

COCKY DOODLE

Mustapha MI££ION

10

FEBRUARY with Cheeky

12

DON'T MOCK! MY COOKING AND MY KITCHEN ARE IN PERFECT ORDER! FOR INSTANCE — HAVE YOU EVER SEEN MICE THERE?

NO...BUT THERE'S A REASON FOR THAT!

THEY TOOK ONE TASTE, AND RUSHED OFF TO SCRUFFBAG TO SURRENDER!

DOH...

WOKE ME UP, THEY DID!

HERE COMES JOGGING JEREMY — HE USED TO PLAY GOLF, BUT PEOPLE KEPT STICKING *HIM* IN THE HOLE INSTEAD OF THE *FLAGSTICK*!

I USED TO BE QUITE GOOD AT GOLF! I USED TO PLAY WITH THAT DUSTMAN — YOU KNOW — THE VERY SHORT-SIGHTED ONE!

YES! IN FACT, HERE HE IS NOW, WITH HIS GOLFING GEAR!

COO-OR! I *WONDERED* WHAT HAD HAPPENED TO THAT CLUB! I THOUGHT I'D LOST IT!

HOWL! NOW YOU KNOW WHY I GAVE UP GOLF! LET ME OUT, YOU SHORT-SIGHTED TWIT!

HO-HO!

I'LL SEE YOU AGAIN IN A FEW PAGES TIME IN MARCH! BUT UNTIL THEN, HERE'S MORE FUN.....

15

The SKATEBOARD SQUAD

17

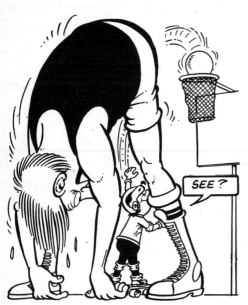

18

22

in "PUTT-ING on the STYLE"

BIDDY'S BEASTLY BLOOMERS

6 MILLION DOLLAR GRAN

28

31

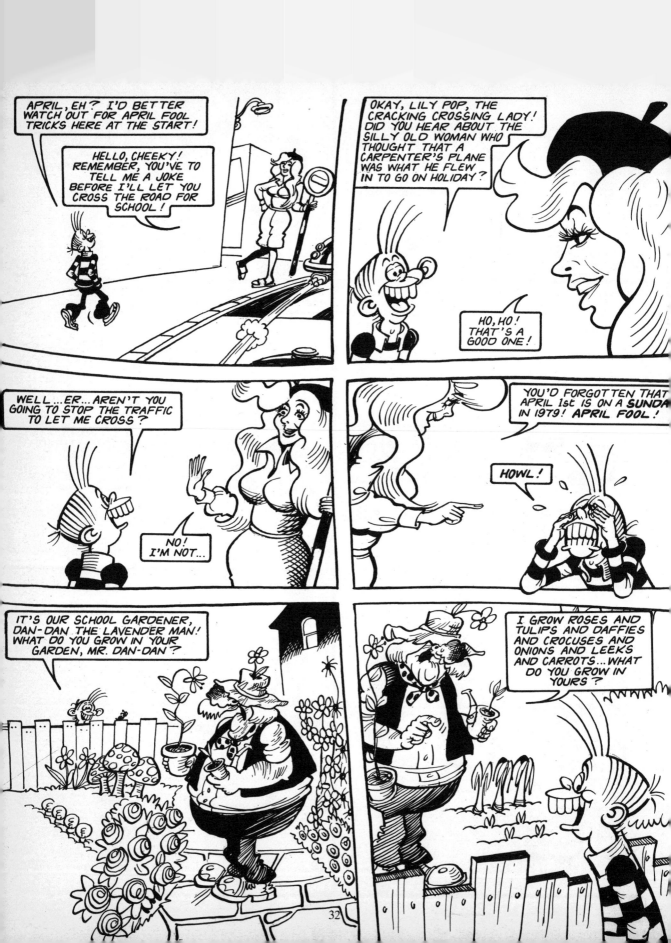

CARTOON GALLERY

BABY BURPO STRIKES!

SOGGY
THE SEA MONSTER

RINGER DINGER ?

in "IT'S A DOGS LIFE"

MAY with Cheeky

45

FIRST, YOU PEEL THE KIPPERS, AND REMOVE THE BONES FROM THE GOOSE-BERRIES! NO, WAIT A MINUTE, YOU REMOVE THE FEATHERS FROM THE GEESEBERRIES! **ER**...

ACTUALLY, IT DOESN'T MATTER **WHAT** YOU DO, BECAUSE NOBODY EVER EATS THE DRATTED THING, ANYWAY! SIGH...

SCHOOL KITCHEN

GREEN FACES (NOT WITH ENVY!)

LARDER

AUNTIE DAISY'S MEALS ARE GOOD FOR THE MEMORY - YOU'LL NEVER FORGET THEM - HOWEVER HARD YOU TRY!

I'M GOING TO TELL YOU ALL ABOUT MY LATEST PET!

THE LIFTS ARE OUT OF ORDER AGAIN!

PERCY'S PARACHUTE CO

WHAT A KNIT!

WHAT'S IN THE BAG, PETULA? IS IT YOUR PET? IS HE CUDDLY? CAN I STROKE HIM, PETULA? CAN I SEE?

SIGH... OKAY, NOSY NORA!

SO'S THE PARACHUTE!

HE'S QUITE AN ORDINARY OLD SNAKE, REALLY!

EEEEEEEEEK!!!!!

LEG ACTION MADE FAMOUS BY WALTER WURX!

HEY, DO-GOOD NORA! NOSY NORA HAS FAINTED! CAN YOU DO A BIT OF GOOD, AND REVIVE HER?

SURE!

49

WE SEEM TO HAVE LOST SIGHT OF YOU! IS THE SURFACE FIRM OR SOFT?

GLUG! GLUG!

...AT A ROUGH GUESS, I WOULD SAY 99% OF THE SURFACE IS FIRM! BUT WHERE I'VE LANDED, IT MUST HAVE RAINED LAST NIGHT! MY FEET ARE SOAKING WET...!

WELL DON'T TAKE YOUR BOOTS OFF! WE BELIEVE THERE'S VERY LITTLE GRAVITY ON THE MOON! YOUR BOOTS ARE WEIGHTED WITH LEAD TO STOP YOU FLOATING AWAY!

NOW HE TELLS ME!

THERE COULD BE SOME TRUTH IN THE RUMOUR THAT THE MOON IS MADE OF CHEESE, PROF! THERE'S A STRONG SMELL OF IT, UP HERE!

IDIOT! THAT'S YOUR SMELLY FEET! GET YOUR BOOTS ON, QUICK!

WHEN YOU'VE DONE THAT, INSIDE THE CABIN YOU'LL FIND A MEANS OF TRANSPORT! WE WANT YOU TO EXPLORE THE SURFACE!

MONITOR

OKAY

I THOUGHT YOU SAID THERE WAS TRANSPORT IN HERE! ALL I'VE FOUND IS A BALLOON AND A BICYCLE PUMP!

THAT'S IT!

WE CALL IT THE 'MOON HOPPER'!

MOON HOPPER

PUMP!

WELL! I SUPPOSE IT BEATS WALKING!

MOON HOPPER

BOUNCE!

HELLO, CONTROL! THERE DOESN'T SEEM TO BE ANY SIGN OF LIFE UP HERE! AT LEAST, NOT ON THE SURFACE! I'M BOUNCING BACK TO THE ROCKET NOW! OVER!

MOON HOP

A FEW BOUNCES LATER...

OKAY, YOU LOT! I'VE DONE ALL THE THINGS YOU WANTED ME TO DO! NOW I'D LIKE TO COME HOME! I'M WORRIED THAT YOU CAN'T GET ME BACK!

HUH! YOU'RE WORRIED! WE'RE WORRIED, TOO! OUR REPUTATION IS AT STAKE! AMUSE YOURSELF FOR A COUPLE OF HOURS WHILE WE WORK OUT THE RETURN FORMULA!

MOO

AND SO OUR CRUSADER SET OFF TO EXPLORE...

BAH! I MUST HAVE BEEN A LUNARTIC TO GET ROPED INTO THIS! WHERE'S MY GOLF CLUBS? GOLF ALWAYS HELPS ME RELAX WHEN I GET TENSE!

BOOT!

53

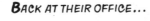

THAT NIGHT, ON THE SCIENTIST'S WAY HOME...

PENNY FOR THE GUY, MISTER!

GOOD GRIEF! I DIDN'T REALISE IT WAS NOVEMBER 5th. HERE'S A COUPLE OF POUNDS, SON! BUY YOURSELF SOME **ROCKETS!** HEH! HEH!

THE MONEY THAT MAN GAVE ME HAS BOUGHT SOME SMASHING ROCKETS, DAD! LOOK AT THAT ONE!

WHOOSH!

THE ROCKET BEGAN TO GO HAYWIRE...

AND LIKE SOME FICKLE FINGER OF FATE, POINTED ITSELF IN THE DIRECTION OF SPACE H.Q.

WOOSH!

WASTE PAPER

THE SMELL OF SMOKE WOKE THE SECURITY GUARD UP, BUT IT WAS TOO LATE...

FIRE! FIRE!

U.K. SPACE H.Q.

NEXT MORNING...

OH NO! WHAT'S HAPPENED?

WHERE'S OUR OFFICE?

A FIREWORK WENT ASTRAY LAST NIGHT! IT MUST HAVE GONE THROUGH AN OPEN WINDOW! EVERY-THING WAS DESTROYED!

THE FILM! THE ONLY FILM OF THE SPACE MISSION HAS BEEN DESTROYED! WHO WILL EVER BELIEVE WE LANDED A MAN ON THE MOON, WITHOUT PROOF OF IT?

NUMB WITH SHOCK

...WHO INDEED, READERS! ALAS, OUT OF THE £403 DONATED BY THE GOVERNMENT TO THE BRITISH SPACE FUND, THERE WASN'T ENOUGH LEFT IN THE KITTY TO REPEAT THE MISSION. THE FOLLOWING YEAR, ON JULY 20th 1969, AMERICA LANDED THEIR MAN ON THE MOON. HOWEVER, THE TRUTH IS, BRITAIN **WAS** FIRST ON THE MOON! BUT WITH-OUT ANY PROOF, WHO WOULD BELIEVE IT? **WOULD YOU?**

ALL SNAILS ARE ALIKE?

NO, THEY'RE NOT! ONLY THREE OF THIS LOT ARE. CAN YOU SPOT THEM?
(ANSWER ON PAGE 110.)

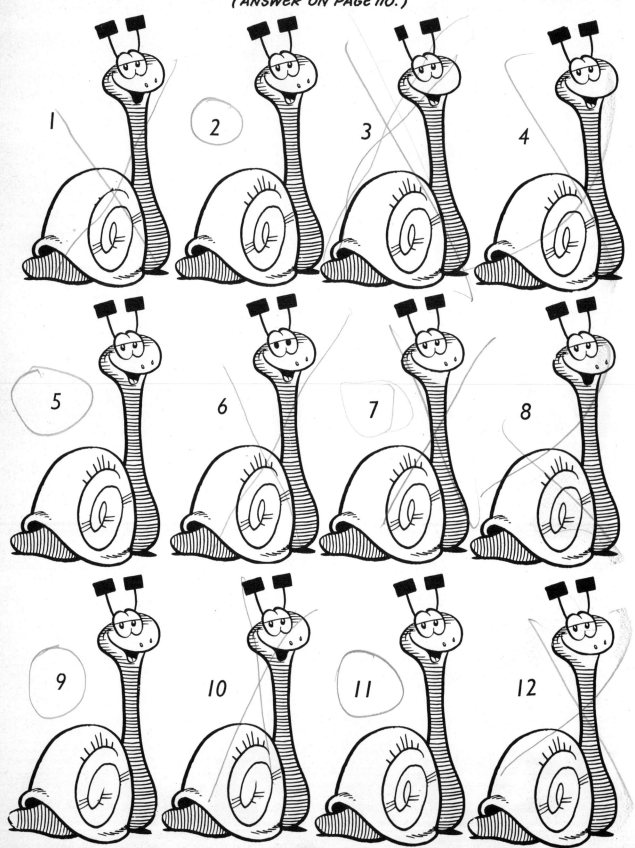

JUNE with Cheeky

Mustapha MI££ION

The ROBOT Olympics

JULY with Cheeky

JULY—WHAT A LOVELY MONTH! WHAT A LOVELY MONTH FOR RUSHING UP TO A MIND-READER AND SHOUTING, *A PENNY FOR MY THOUGHTS!*

YUP—US COWBOYS IS BROUGHT UP ROUGH—MY MOTHER DIDN'T PUT *BABY* POWDER ALL OVER ME, SHE PUT *GUN*-POWDER!

COO-OO...! WHAT HAPPENED?

SHE PATTED ME ON THE BACK, AND BLEW MY HAT OFF!

OH, BOY! I DON'T BELIEVE *THAT*, FOR A START!

PSSST! WANNA BUY A PAIR OF DARK GLASSES? YOU'LL NOT SEE THEM AT THIS PRICE ANYWHERE ELSE!

LET ME SEE... *HAH!* AS I THOUGHT!

YOU'D NOT SEE *ANYTHING, ANYWHERE,* WITH THESE! THEY'RE ORDINARY OLD GLASSES, PAINTED BLACK!

GULP! JUST REMEMBERED AN URGENT APPOINTMENT! MUST DASH!

TIM'LL FIX IT

THE DOORS ARE OPEN...

RINGER DINGER ?

in "A SLICE OF BAD LUCK"

SOGGY
THE SEA MONSTER

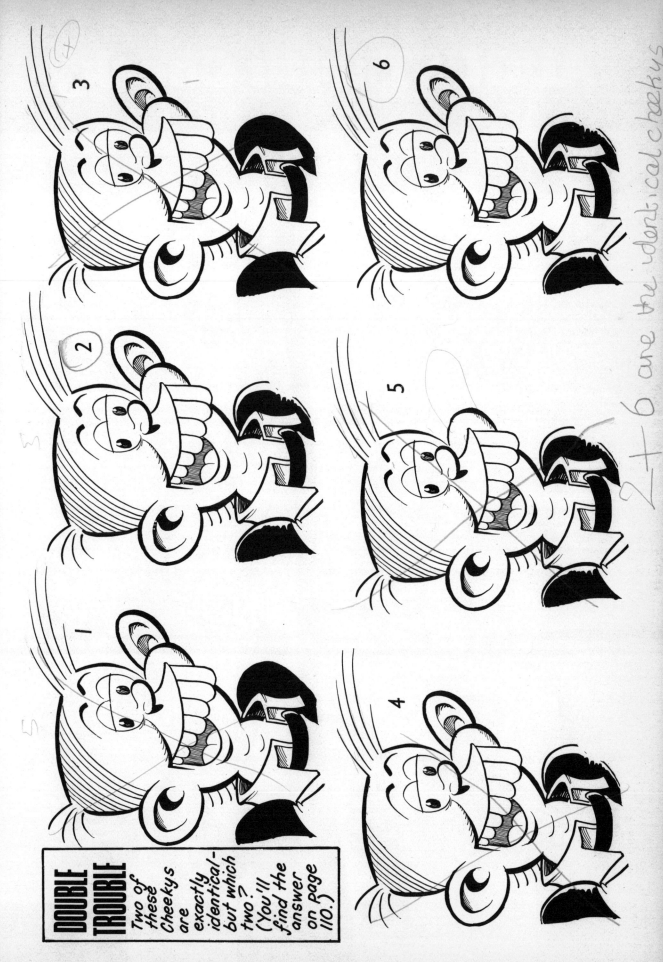

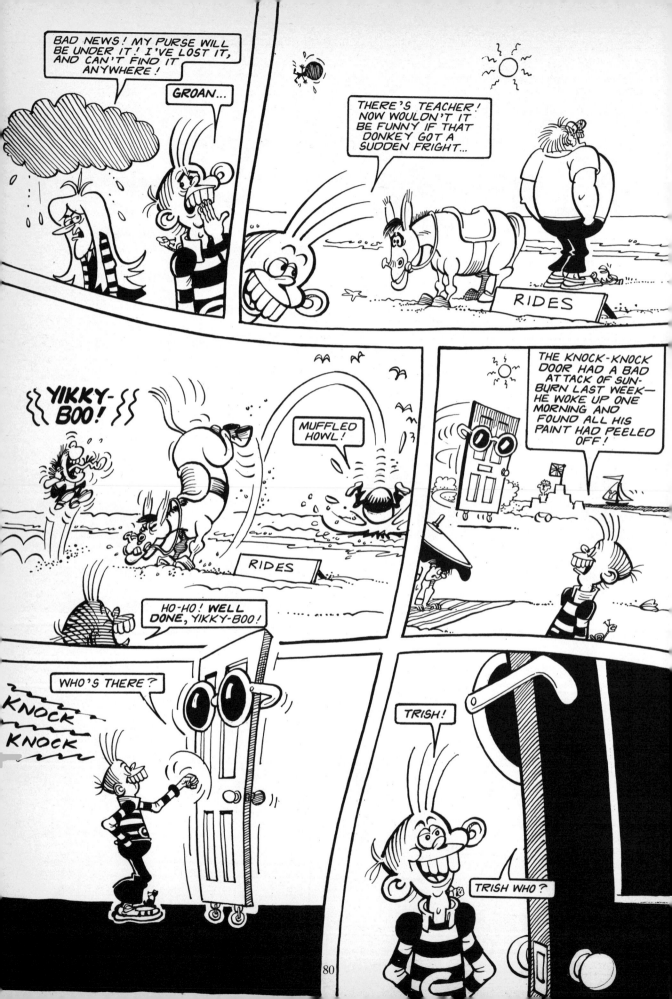

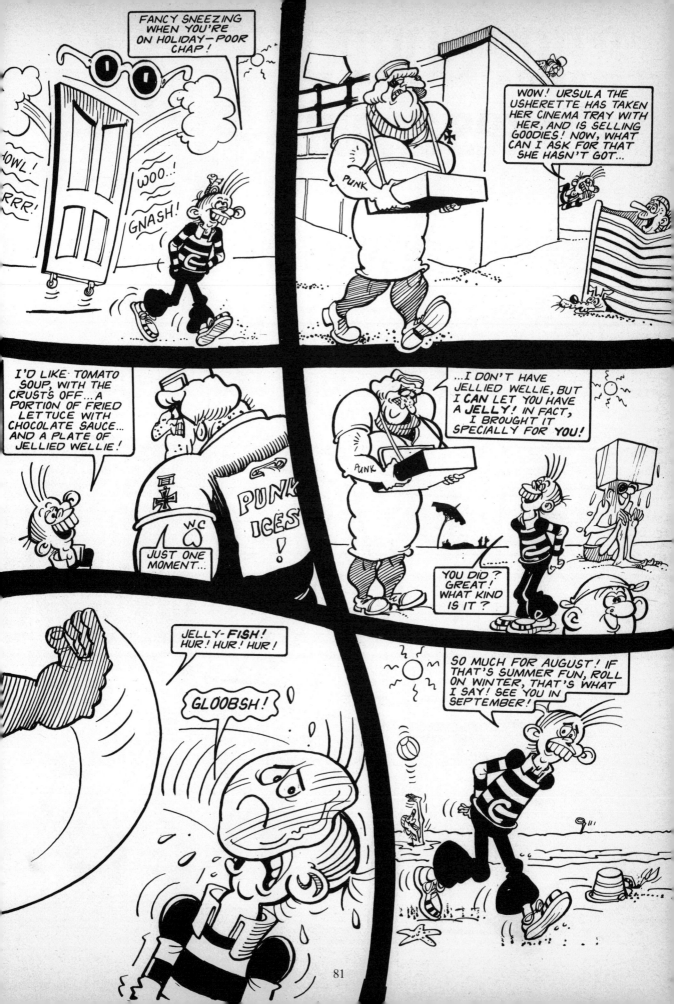

BABY BURPO strikes again

CHEEKY STILL NOT SEEN ME TAKING OVER FROM HIM, SO ME TALK SOME MORE TO HIS PALS!

I DON'T BELIEVE IT! THAT'S THE FIRST TIME I'VE EVER BEEN BEATEN!

HERE KNOCK-KNOCK DOOR! OOOH! ME CAN'T REACH!

KNOCK! KNOCK!

WHO'S THERE?

TICH!

TICH WHO?

OOH, THAT NASTY COLD YOU GOT!

OOOH! HOWL! GRR! BAH!

TA FOR LETTING BABY STAND ON YOUR BACK, WALTER WURX!

THAT'S ALL RIGHT!

82

CREEPY SLEEPY TALE

A NATIONAL ELF

BIDDY'S BEASTLY BLOOMERS

91

THE SKATEBOARD SQUAD

GREAT STUFF, WIPE-OUT!

THAT DOG WOULD BE A BIG HIT IN OUR CIRCUS, SID!

DUH-H! SO WHAT, CYRIL? I DON'T GET IT!

A STAR LIKE THAT WOULD DRAW IN THE CROWDS, AND CROWDS MEAN MONEY!

DUH-H! NOW I GET IT! NICE ONE, CYRIL!

HEY! I CAN'T SEE!

DOGGONE!

I CAN SEE THAT, BUT WHERE DID HE GO?

GONE!

THEY'VE KIDNAPPED WIPE-OUT, SKATIE— AFTER THEM!

THIS'LL STOP YOU PESKY KIDS CHASING US!

OOH, NO IT WON'T!

BUMPITY-BUMP-BUMP-BUMP!

OOH, YES IT WILL – THEY'VE GOT AWAY!

AND WE CAN'T CHASE THEM ON BOARDS WITH SQUARE WHEELS!

SOON, AT THE CIRCUS...

RIGHT, DOG – YOU'RE GONNA STAR IN OUR CIRCUS AN' BE A BIG HIT!

OR YOU'LL **DIE!**

PHOOEY! TRICKED BY A WATER PISTOL!

OR SHOULD I SAY **DYE** – CAN'T HAVE YOU BEING RECOGNISED!

SQUIRT!

SOON...

HEH, HEH! YOU'RE A **DIRTY DOG** NOW!

MUTTER, MUTTER!

OCTOBER with Cheeky

6,000,000$ GRAN

102

104

BIDDY'S BEASTLY BLOOMERS

NOVEMBER with Cheeky

BIDDY'S BEASTLY BLOOMERS

in "A CHRISTMAS TREE-T"

SOGGY The SEA MONSTER

DECEMBER with Cheeky

DECEMBER, ALREADY! I WONDER WHAT SOME OF MY PALS ARE HOPING TO GET FOR CHRISTMAS?

I'M A-WANTIN'A A PAIR OF BOXING GLOVES!

EH? WHAT WOULD A COWBOY WANT WITH BOXING GLOVES?

AIN'T YOU EVER HEARD OF A COW-PUNCHER?

GROAN... HE GOT ME AGAIN!

GULP! HERE COMES LOUISE, WITH A FARAWAY LOOK! I WISH SHE WOULD GO AND JOIN IT!

THERE'S ONLY ONE THING I WANT FOR CHRISTMAS!

WHAT'S THAT, HA-HA! A BOOK? A DRESS? A RABBIT-HUTCH?

NO... TRY AGAIN, CHEEKY, MY LITTLE CUDDLY COOCHI-COO!

A DOLL'S PRAM? A KANGAROO? A PLATE OF COO AND CHIPS?

125

126